CW00816403

ICE Conditions of Contract for Minor Works

Third Edition

CONDITIONS OF CONTRACT, APPENDIX AND FORM
OF AGREEMENT FOR USE IN CONNECTION WITH
MINOR WORKS OF CIVIL ENGINEERING CONSTRUCTION

The Institution of Civil Engineers
Association of Consulting Engineers
Civil Engineering Contractors Association

Published by Thomas Telford Publishing, Thomas Telford Limited, 1 Heron Quay, London E14 4JD on behalf of

The Chief Executive and Secretary
The Institution of Civil Engineers
One Great George Street
London SWIP 3AA

The Chief Executive
Association of Consulting Engineers
Alliance House
12 Caxton Street
London SW1H 0QL

The Director
Civil Engineering Contractors Association
Construction House
56-64 Leonard Street
London EC2A 4JX

The first and second editions were approved by The Institution of Civil Engineers, the Association of Consulting Engineers and the Federation of Civil Engineering Contractors.
First edition 1988
Second edition 1995, reprinted 1998 with an amendment
Third edition was approved by The Institution of Civil Engineers, the Association of Consulting Engineers and the Federation of Civil Engineering Contractors April 2001.
Third edition 2001, reprinted 2004 with an amendment

The Institution of Civil Engineers, the Association of Consulting Engineers and the Civil Engineering Contractors Association have, as sponsoring bodies, approved this revised third edition of the document commonly known as the ICE Conditions of Contract for Minor Works, for all minor works of civil engineering construction. A permanent joint committee of the sponsoring bodies has prepared and will keep under review the use of this document and will consider any suggestions for amendment, which should be addressed to the Chief Executive and Secretary (CCSJC), The Institution of Civil Engineers, One Great George Street, London SW1P 3AA. Revision to the document will be made when such action seems warranted.

9 8 7 6 5 4 3 2

ISBN 0 7277 2940 3

Printed and bound in Great Britain by Formara Ltd., Essex

CONTENTS

Associated publications referred to in the Contract

ICE Arbitration Procedure 1997
ICE Appendix (2001) to "The Scottish Arbitration Code 1999"
ICE Conciliation Procedure 1999
ICE Adjudication Procedure (1997)

Other ICE Conditions of Contract publications

ICE Conditions of Contract 7th Edition
Guidance Notes to the ICE Conditions of Contract 7th Edition
ICE Design and Construct Conditions of Contract 2nd Edition
Guidance Notes to the ICE Design and Construct Conditions of Contract 2nd
Edition

INDEX

ICE Conditions of Contract for Minor Works

1 DEFINITIONS AND INTERPRETATION

Definitions

1.1 "Works" means all the work necessary for the completion of the Contract including any variations ordered by the Engineer.

1.2 "Contract" means the Agreement if any together with these Conditions of Contract the Appendix and other items listed in the Contract Schedule.

1.3 "Cost" (except where otherwise defined for 'cost plus' contracts, see Appendix paragraph 2) means all expenditure properly incurred or to be incurred whether on or off the Site including overhead finance and other charges (including loss of interest) properly allocatable thereto but does not include any allowance for profit.

1.4 "Site" means the lands and other places on under in or through which the Works are to be constructed and any other lands or places provided by the Employer for the purposes of the Contract together with such other places as may be designated in the Contract or subsequently agreed by the Engineer as forming part of the Site.

1.5 "Excepted Risks" are

(a) the use or occupation by the Employer his agents servants or other contractors (not being employed by the Contractor) of any part of the Permanent Works

(b) any fault defect error or omission in the design of the Works (other than a design provided by the Contractor pursuant to his obligations under the Contract)

(c) riot war invasion act of foreign enemies or hostilities (whether war be declared or not)

(d) civil war rebellion revolution insurrection or military or usurped power

(e) ionizing radiations or contamination by radioactivity from any nuclear fuel or from any nuclear waste from the combustion of nuclear fuel radioactive toxic explosive or other hazardous properties of any explosive nuclear assembly or nuclear component hereof

and

(f) pressure waves caused by aircraft or other aerial devices travelling at sonic or supersonic speeds.

Headings and marginal notes

1.6 The headings and marginal notes in the Conditions of Contract shall not be deemed to be part thereof or be taken into consideration in the interpretation or construction thereof or the Contract.

Communications in writing

1.7 Communications which under the Contract are required to be 'in writing' may be hand-written typewritten or printed and sent by hand post telex cable facsimile or other means resulting in a permanent record.

2   ENGINEER

Engineer to be a named individual   2.1   The Employer shall appoint and notify to the Contractor in writing a named individual to act as the Engineer. If at any time the Engineer is unable to continue the duties required by the Contract the Employer shall forthwith appoint a replacement and shall so notify the Contractor in writing.

Delegation   2.2   The Engineer may appoint a named Resident Engineer and/or other suitably experienced person to watch and inspect the Works and the Engineer may delegate to such person in writing any of the powers of the Engineer herein other than those in Clause 11 or Addendum A provided that prior notice in writing is given to the Contractor.

Instructions   2.3   The Engineer shall have power to give instructions for

(a)   any variation to the Works including any addition thereto or omission therefrom

(b)   carrying out any test or investigation

(c)   the suspension of the Works or any part of the Works in accordance with Clause 2.6

(d)   any change in the intended sequence of the Works

(e)   measures necessary to overcome or deal with any obstruction or condition falling within Clause 3.8

(f)   the removal and/or re-execution of any work or materials not in accordance with the Contract

(g)   the elucidation or explanation of any matter to enable the Contractor to meet his obligations under the Contract

(h)   the exclusion from the Site of any person employed thereon which power shall not be exercised unreasonably.

Exercise of Delegated Powers   2.4   The Engineer or Resident Engineer and/or other suitably experienced person who exercises any delegated power shall upon the written request of the Contractor specify in writing under which of the foregoing powers any instruction is given. If the Contractor is dissatisfied with any such instruction he shall be entitled to refer the matter to the Engineer for his decision pursuant to Clause 11 or Addendum A.

Dayworks   2.5   The Engineer may order in writing that any work shall be executed on a daywork basis. Subject to the production of proper records the Contractor shall then be entitled to be paid in accordance with a Daywork Schedule included in the Contract or otherwise in accordance with the 'Schedule of Dayworks carried out incidental to Contract Work' issued by the Civil Engineering Contractors Association and current at the date the work is carried out.

Engineer may Suspend the Progress of the Works 2.6 (1) The Engineer may order the suspension of the progress of the Works or any part thereof

    (a) for the proper execution of the work

    (b) for the safety of the Works or any part thereof

    (c) by reason of weather conditions

and in such event may issue such instructions as may in his opinion be necessary to protect and secure the Works during the period of suspension.

(2) If permission to resume work is not given by the Engineer within a period of 60 days from the date of the written Order of Suspension then the Contractor may serve a written notice on the Engineer requiring permission to proceed with the Works within 14 days from the receipt of such notice. Subject to the Contractor not being in default under the Contract the Engineer shall grant such permission and if such permission is not granted the Contractor may by a further written notice served on the Engineer elect to treat the suspension where it affects a part of the Works as an omission under Clause 2.3(a) or where the whole of the Works is suspended as an abandonment of the Contract by the Employer.

Parties bound by Engineer's instructions 2.7 Each party shall be bound by and give effect to every instruction or decision of the Engineer unless and until it is altered or amended by agreement or other determination pursuant to Clause 11.

3   **GENERAL OBLIGATIONS**

Contractor to perform and complete the Works 3.1 The Contractor shall perform and complete the Works and shall (subject to any provision in the Contract) provide all supervision labour materials plant transport and temporary works which may be necessary therefor.

Responsibility for care of the Works 3.2 (1) The Contractor shall take full responsibility for the care of the Works from the starting date until 14 days after the Engineer issues a Certificate of Practical Completion for the whole of the Works pursuant to Clause 4.5.

(2) If the Engineer issues a Certificate of Practical Completion in respect of any part of the Works before completion of the whole of the Works the Contractor shall cease to be responsible for the care of that part of the Works 14 days thereafter and the responsibility of its care shall then pass to the Employer.

(3) The Contractor shall take full responsibility for the care of any outstanding work which he has undertaken to finish during the Defects Correction Period until such outstanding work is complete.

Contractor to repair and make good 3.3 (1) In case any damage loss or injury from any cause whatsoever (save and except the Excepted Risks) shall happen to the Works or any part thereof while the Contractor is responsible for their care the Contractor shall at his own cost repair and make good the same so that at completion the Works shall be in good order and condition and conform in every respect with the requirements of the Contract and the Engineer's instructions.

(2) To the extent that any damage loss or injury arises from any of the Excepted Risks the Contractor shall if required by the Engineer repair and make good the same at the expense of the Employer.

(3) The Contractor shall also be liable for any damage to the Works occasioned by him in the course of any operations carried out by him for the purpose of completing outstanding work or complying with his obligations under Clauses 4.7 and 5.2.

Contractor's authorized representative 3.4 The Contractor shall notify the Engineer of the person duly authorized to receive instructions on behalf of the Contractor.

Setting out and safety of site operations 3.5 The Contractor shall take full responsibility for the setting out of the Works and for the adequacy stability and safety of his site operations and methods of construction.

Engineer to provide necessary information 3.6 Subject to Clause 3.5 the Engineer shall be responsible for the provision of any instructions drawings or other information necessary for the proper and adequate construction and completion of the Works.

Contractor's responsibility for design 3.7 (1) The Contractor shall not be responsible for the design of the Works except where expressly stated in the Contract.

(2) The Contractor shall be responsible for the design of any temporary works other than temporary works designed by the Engineer.

(3) The Contractor shall exercise all reasonable skill care and diligence in designing any part of the permanent Works for which he is responsible.

Adverse physical conditions and artificial obstructions—delay and extra cost 3.8 (1) If during the carrying out of the Works the Contractor encounters any artificial obstruction or physical condition (other than a weather condition or a condition due to weather) which obstruction or condition could not in his opinion reasonably have been foreseen by an experienced contractor the Contractor shall as early as practicable give written notice thereof to the Engineer.

(2) If in the opinion of the Engineer such obstruction or condition could not reasonably have been foreseen by an experienced contractor then the Engineer shall certify a fair and reasonable sum and the Employer shall pay such sum to cover the cost of performing any additional work or using any additional plant or equipment together with a reasonable percentage addition in respect of profit as a result of

(a) complying with any instructions which the Engineer may issue

and/or

(b) taking proper and reasonable measures to overcome or deal with the obstruction or condition in the absence of instructions from the Engineer

together with such sum as shall be agreed as the additional cost to the Contractor of the delay or disruption arising therefrom. Failing agreement of such sums the Engineer shall determine the fair and reasonable sum to be paid.

Facilities for other contractors 3.9 The Contractor shall in accordance with requirements of the Engineer afford reasonable facilities for any other contractor employed by the Employer and for any other properly authorized authority employed on the Site.

4   STARTING AND COMPLETION

Starting date to be notified in writing   4.1   The starting date shall be the date specified in the Appendix or if no date is specified a date to be notified by the Engineer in writing being within a reasonable time and in any event within 28 days after the date of acceptance of the Tender. The Contractor shall begin the Works at or as soon as reasonably possible after the starting date.

Period for Completion   4.2   The period or periods for completion shall be as stated in the Appendix or such extended time as may be granted under Clause 4.4 and shall commence on the starting date.

Contractor's programme   4.3   The Contractor shall within 14 days after the starting date if so required provide a programme of his intended activities. The Contractor shall at all times proceed with the Works with due expedition and reasonably in accordance with his programme or any modification thereof which he may provide or which the Engineer may request.

Extension of period for completion   4.4   If the progress of the Works or any part thereof is delayed for any of the following reasons

     (a)   an instruction given under Clause 2.3(a)(c) or (d)

     (b)   an instruction given under Clause 2.3(b) where the test or investigation fails to disclose non-compliance with the Contract

     (c)   encountering an obstruction or condition falling within Clause 3.8 and/or an instruction given under Clause 2.3(e)

     (d)   delay in receipt by the Contractor of necessary instructions drawings or other information

     (e)   failure by the Employer to give adequate access to the Works or possession of land required to perform the Works

     (f)   delay in receipt by the Contractor of materials to be provided by the Employer under the Contract

     (g)   exceptional adverse weather

     (h)   any delay impediment prevention or default by the Employer

     (i)   other special circumstances of any kind whatsoever outside the control of the Contractor

then provided that the Contractor has taken all reasonable steps to avoid or minimize the delay the Engineer shall upon a written request by the Contractor promptly by notice in writing grant such extension of the period for completion of the whole or part of the Works as may in his opinion be reasonable. The extended period or periods for completion shall be subject to regular review provided that no such review shall result in a decrease in any extension of time already granted by the Engineer.

Certificate of Practical Completion of Works or part of Works   4.5   (1)   Practical completion of the whole of the Works shall occur when the Works reach a state when notwithstanding any defect or outstanding items therein they are taken or are fit to be taken into use or possession by the Employer.

     (2)   Similarly practical completion of part of the Works may also occur but only if it is fit for such part to be taken into use or possession independently of the remainder.

(3) The Engineer shall upon the Contractor's request promptly certify in writing the date on which the Works or any part thereof has reached practical completion or otherwise advise the Contractor in writing of the work necessary to achieve such completion.

Liquidated damages   4.6   If by the end of the period or extended period or periods for completion the Works have not reached practical completion the Contractor shall be liable to the Employer in the sum stated in the Appendix as liquidated damages for every week (or *pro rata* for part of a week) during which the Works so remain uncompleted up to the limit stated in the Appendix. Similarly where part or parts of the Works so remain uncompleted the Contractor shall be liable to the Employer in the sum stated in the Appendix reduced in proportion to the value of those parts which have been certified as complete provided that the said limit shall not be reduced.

Provided that if after liquidated damages have become payable in respect of any part of the Works the Engineer issues a variation order under Clause 2.3(a) or an artificial obstruction or physical condition within the meaning of Clause 3.8 is encountered or any other situation outside the Contractor's control arises any of which in the opinion of the Engineer results in further delay to that part of the Works

     (a)   the Engineer shall so inform the Contractor and the Employer in writing

and

     (b)   the Employer's further entitlement to liquidated damages in respect of that part of the Works shall be suspended until the Engineer notifies the Contractor and the Employer in writing that the further delay has come to an end.

Such suspension shall not invalidate any entitlement to liquidated damages which accrued before the period of delay started to run and any monies deducted or paid in accordance with this Clause may be retained by the Employer without incurring interest thereon under Clause 7.8.

Rectification of defects   4.7   The Contractor shall rectify any defects and complete any outstanding items in the Works or any part thereof which reach practical completion promptly thereafter or in such a manner and/or time as may be agreed or otherwise accepted by the Engineer. The Contractor shall maintain any parts which reach practical completion in the condition required by the Contract until practical completion of the whole of the Works fair wear and tear excepted.

5   DEFECTS

Definition of Defects Correction Period   5.1   'Defects Correction Period' means the period stated in the Appendix which period shall run from the date certified as practical completion of the whole of the Works.

Cost of remedying defects   5.2   If any defects appear in the Works during the Defects Correction Period which are due to the use of materials or workmanship not in accordance with the Contract the Engineer shall give written notice thereof and the Contractor shall make good the same at his own cost.

Remedy for Contractor's failure to correct defects   5.3   If any such defects are not corrected within a reasonable time by the Contractor the Employer may after giving 14 days written notice to the Contractor employ others to correct the same and the cost thereof shall be payable by the Contractor to the Employer.

Engineer to certify completion	5.4	Upon the expiry of the Defects Correction Period and when any outstanding work notified to the Contractor under Clause 5.2 has been made good the Engineer shall upon the written request of the Contractor certify the date on which the Contractor completed his obligations under the Contract to the Engineer's satisfaction.
Unfulfilled obligations	5.5	Nothing in Clause 5 shall affect the rights of either party in respect of defects appearing after the Defects Correction Period.

6   ADDITIONAL PAYMENTS

Engineer to Determine additional sums and deductions	6.1	If the Contractor carries out additional works or incurs additional cost including any cost arising from delay or disruption to the progress of the Works as a result of any of the matters referred to in paragraphs (a) (b) (d) (e) (f) or (h) of Clause 4.4 the Engineer shall certify and the Employer shall pay to the Contractor such additional sum as the Engineer after consultation with the Contractor considers fair and reasonable. Likewise the Engineer shall determine a fair and reasonable deduction to be made in respect of any omission of work.
Valuation of additional work	6.2	In determining a fair and reasonable sum under Clause 6.1 for additional work the Engineer shall have regard to the prices contained in the Contract.

7   PAYMENT

Valuation of the Works	7.1	The Works shall be valued as provided for in the Contract.
Monthly statements	7.2	Unless otherwise agreed the Contractor shall submit to the Engineer at intervals of not less than one month commencing within one month after the starting date of the Works a statement showing the estimated value of the Works executed up to the end of that period together with a list of any goods or materials delivered to the Site and their value and any other items which the Contractor considers should be included in an interim certificate.
Interim payments	7.3	Within 25 days of the delivery of such statement the Engineer shall certify and within 28 days of the same date the Employer shall pay to the Contractor (after deducting any previous payments on account) such sum as the Engineer considers is properly due less retention at the rate of and up to the limit set out in the Appendix. Until practical completion of the whole of the Works the Engineer shall not be required to certify any payment less than the sum stated in the Appendix as the minimum amount of interim certificate. The Engineer may by any certificate delete correct or modify any sum previously certified by him. The payments become due on certification with the final date for payment being 28 days after the date of delivery of the Contractor's monthly statement.
Payment of retention money	7.4	One half of the retention money shall be certified by the Engineer and paid to the Contractor within 14 days after the date on which the Engineer issues a certificate of practical completion of the whole of the Works.
	7.5	The final date for payment of the remainder of the retention money to be paid to the Contractor is 14 days after the issue of the Engineer's certificate under Clause 5.4.
Contractor to submit final account	7.6	Within 28 days after the issue of the Engineer's certificate under Clause 5.4 the Contractor shall submit a final account to the Engineer together with any documentation reasonably required to enable the Engineer to ascertain the final contract value. Within 42 days after the receipt of this information the Engineer shall issue the final certificate. The amount payable by the Employer shall become due on certification. The final date for payment is 14 days later.

7.7 The final certificate shall save in the case of fraud or dishonesty relating to or affecting any matter dealt with in the certificate be conclusive evidence as to the sum due to the Contractor under or arising out of the Contract (subject only to Clause 7.11) unless either party has within 28 days after the issue of the final certificate given notice pursuant to Clause 11 or Addendum A.

Interest on overdue payments **7.8** In the event of failure by the Engineer to certify or the Employer to make payment in accordance with the Contract or any decision of an adjudicator or any finding of an arbitrator to such effect the Employer shall pay to the Contractor interest compounded monthly for each day on which any payment is overdue or which should have been certified and paid at a rate equivalent to 2% per annum above the base lending rate of the bank specified in the Appendix.

Certificates and payment notices **7.9** Every certificate issued by the Engineer pursuant to this Clause shall be sent to the Employer and on the Employer's behalf to the Contractor. By this certificate the Employer shall give notice to the Contractor specifying the amount (if any) of the payment proposed to be made and the basis on which it was calculated.

Notice of intention to withhold payment **7.10** Where a payment under Clause 7.3 or 7.6 is to differ from that certified or the Employer is to withhold payment after the final date for payment of a sum due under the Contract the Employer shall notify the Contractor in writing not less than one day before the final date for payment specifying the amount proposed to be withheld and the ground for withholding payment or if there is more than one ground each ground and the amount attributable to it.

Value Added Tax **7.11** (1) The Contractor shall be deemed not to have allowed in his tender for the tax payable by him as a taxable person to the Commissioners of Customs and Excise being tax chargeable on any taxable supplies to the Employer which are to be made under the Contract.

(2) All certificates issued by the Engineer under Clauses 7.3 to 7.7 shall be net of Value Added Tax.

(3) In addition to the payments due under such certificates the Employer shall separately identify and pay to the Contractor any Value Added Tax properly chargeable by the Commissioners of Customs and Excise on the supply to the Employer of any goods and/or services by the Contractor under the Contract.

8 **ASSIGNMENT AND SUB-CONTRACTING**

Assignment **8.1** (1) Neither the Employer nor the Contractor shall assign the Contract or any part thereof or any benefit or interest therein or thereunder without the written consent of the other party which consent shall not unreasonably be withheld.

Third party rights (2) Nothing in this contract confers or purports to confer on any third party any benefit or any right pursuant to the Contracts (Rights of Third Parties) Act 1999 to enforce any term of the Contract.

No sub-contracting without Engineer's Consent **8.2** The Contractor shall not sub-contract the whole of the Works. The Contractor shall not sub-contract any part of the Works without the consent of the Engineer which consent shall not unreasonably be withheld.

Contractor responsible for sub-contractors **8.3** The Contractor shall be responsible for any acts defaults or neglects of any sub-contractor his agents servants or workmen in the execution of the Works or any part thereof as if they were the acts defaults or neglects of the Contractor.

9   STATUTORY OBLIGATIONS

Contractor to comply with statutory requirements

9.1   The Contractor shall subject to Clause 9.3 comply with and give all notices required by any statute statutory instrument rule or order or any regulation or by-law applicable to the construction of the Works (hereinafter called 'the statutory requirements') and shall pay all fees and charges which are payable in respect thereof.

Employer to obtain consents

9.2   The Employer shall be responsible for obtaining in due time any consent approval licence or permission but only to the extent that the same may be necessary for the Works in their permanent form.

Contractor's exemption from liability to comply with statutes

9.3   The Contractor shall not be liable for any failure to comply with the statutory requirements where and to the extent that such failure results from the Contractor having carried out the Works in accordance with the Contract or with any instruction of the Engineer.

10   LIABILITIES AND INSURANCE

Insurance of the Works

10.1   (1)   If so stated in the Appendix the Contractor shall maintain insurance in the joint names of the Employer and the Contractor in respect of the Works (including for the purpose of Clause 10 any unfixed materials or other things delivered to the Site for incorporation therein) to their full value against all loss or damage from whatever cause arising (other than the Excepted Risks) for which he is responsible under the terms of the Contract.

(2)   Such insurance shall be effected in such a manner that the Employer and Contractor are covered for the period stipulated in Clause 3.2 and are also covered for loss or damage arising during the Defects Correction Period from such cause occurring prior to the commencement of the Defects Correction Period and for any loss or damage occasioned by the Contractor in the course of any operation carried out by him for the purpose of complying with his obligations under Clauses 4.7 and 5.2.

(3)   The Contractor shall not be liable to insure against the necessity for the repair or reconstruction of any work constructed with materials or workmanship not in accordance with the requirements of the Contract.

(4)   Any amounts not insured or not recovered from insurers whether as excesses carried under the policy or otherwise shall be borne by the Contractor or the Employer in accordance with their respective responsibilities under Clauses 3.2 and 3.3.

Contractor to indemnify the Employer

10.2   The Contractor shall indemnify and keep the Employer indemnified against all losses and claims for injury or damage to any person or property whatsoever (save for the matters for which the Contractor is responsible under Clause 3.2) which may arise out of or in consequence of the Works and against all claims demands proceedings damages costs charges and expenses whatsoever in respect thereof or in relation thereto subject to Clauses 10.3 and 10.4.

10.3   The liability of the Contractor to indemnify the Employer under Clause 10.2 shall be reduced proportionately to the extent that the act or neglect of the Engineer or the Employer his servants his agents or other contractors not employed by the Contractor may have contributed to the said loss injury or damage.

10.4 The Contractor shall not be liable for or in respect of or to indemnify the Employer against any compensation or damage for or with respect to

(a) damage to crops being on the Site (save in so far as possession has not been given to the Contractor)

(b) the use or occupation of land (which has been provided by the Employer) by the Works or any part thereof or for the purpose of constructing completing and maintaining the Works (including consequent loss of crops) or interference whether temporary or permanent with any right of way light air or water or other easement or quasi easement which are the unavoidable result of the construction of the Works in accordance with the Contract

(c) the right of the Employer to construct the Works or any part thereof on over under in or through any land

(d) damage which is the unavoidable result of the construction of the Works in accordance with the Contract

(e) death or injury to persons or loss of or damage to property resulting from any act or neglect or breach of statutory duty done or committed by the Engineer or the Employer his agents servants or other contractors (not being employed by the Contractor) or for or in respect of any claims demands proceedings damages costs charges and expenses in respect thereof or in relation thereto.

Employer to indemnify Contractor **10.5** The Employer shall indemnify and keep indemnified the Contractor from and against all claims demands proceedings damages costs charges and expenses in respect of the matters referred to in Clause 10.4. Provided always that the Employer's liability to indemnify the Contractor under paragraph (e) of Clause 10.4 shall be reduced proportionately to the extent that the act or neglect of the Contractor or his sub-contractors servants or agents may have contributed to the said injury or damage.

Employer to approve insurance **10.6** The Contractor shall throughout the execution of the Works maintain insurance against damage loss or injury for which he is liable under Clause 10.2 subject to the exceptions provided by Clauses 10.3 and 10.4. Such insurance shall be effected with an insurer and in terms approved by the Employer (which approval shall not be unreasonably withheld) for at least the amount stated in the Appendix. The terms of such insurance shall include a provision whereby in the event of any claim in respect of which the Contractor would be entitled to receive indemnity under the policy being brought or made against the Employer the insurer will indemnify the Employer against any such claims and any costs charges and expenses in respect thereof.

Contractor to produce policies of insurance **10.7** Both the Employer and the Contractor shall comply with the terms of any policy issued in connection with the Contract and shall whenever required produce to the Employer the policy or policies of insurance and the receipts for the payment of the current premiums.

11 **DISPUTES**

Settlement of disputes **11.1** If any dispute or difference of any kind whatsoever shall arise between the Employer and the Contractor in connection with or arising out of the Contract or the carrying out of the Works (excluding a dispute under Clause 7.11 but including a dispute as to any act or omission of the Engineer) whether arising during the progress of the Works or after their completion it shall be settled according to the provisions in Addendum A.

12 APPLICATION TO SCOTLAND AND NORTHERN IRELAND

Application to Scotland **12.1** If the Works are situated in Scotland (and unless the Contract otherwise provides) the Contract shall in all respects be construed and operate as a Scottish contract and shall be interpreted in accordance with Scots Law and the provisions of sub-clause (2) of this Clause shall apply.

12.2 In the application of these Conditions and in particular Addendum A hereof

(a) any reference to arbitration under this Clause shall be conducted in accordance with the law of Scotland "The Scottish Arbitration Code 1999" prepared by the Scottish Council for International Arbitration, the Chartered Institute of Arbitrators (Scottish Branch) and the Scottish Building Contract Committee together with the ICE Appendix (2001) thereto or any amendment to or modification of the Appendix being in force at the time of appointment of the arbitrator. Such arbitrator shall have full power to open up review and revise any decision, opinion, instruction, direction, certificate or valuation of the Engineer or an adjudicator

(b) for any reference to the "Notice to Refer" there shall be substituted reference to the 'Notice of Arbitration'

(c) the existing Addendum Clause A.10 shall be deleted and replaced with the new Addendum Clause A.10 below

" Appointment of arbitrator

A.10 (a) The arbitral tribunal shall be appointed by agreement of the parties.

President or Vice-President to act

(b) Failing agreement of the parties as aforesaid at sub-clause (a) above the following shall apply.

(i) Reference to Articles 3.5 and 3.6 of the Code to the Chairman of the Institute of Arbitrators (Scottish Branch) and to the Chairman of the Scottish Council for International Arbitration shall be deemed to be a reference to the President of the Institution of Civil Engineers as defined at (ii) below.

(ii) "President" means the President for the time being of the Institution of Civil Engineers or any Vice President acting on his behalf or such other person as may have been nominated in the arbitration agreement to appoint the arbitrator in default of agreement between the parties.
"

(d) the existing Addendum Clause A.11 shall be deleted and replaced with new Addendum Clause A.11 below

" Arbitration – procedure and powers

A.11 (a) Neither party shall be limited in the arbitration to the evidence or arguments put to the Engineer or to any adjudicator pursuant to Addendum Clause A.2 or A.6 respectively.

(b) Unless the parties otherwise agree in writing any reference to arbitration may proceed notwithstanding that the Works are not then complete or alleged to be complete.
"

(e) notwithstanding any of the other provisions of these Conditions or of the Code (including in particular Articles 22.7 and 22.8) nothing therein shall be construed as excluding recourse to the Court of Sessions under Section 3 of the Administration of Justice of (Scotland) Act 1972

(f)   where the Employer or the Contractor wishes to register the award of an arbitrator or the decision of an adjudicator in the Books of Council and Session for preservation and execution the other party shall on being requested to do so forthwith consent to such registration by subscribing the said decision before a witness and

(g)   the existing Appendix to the Conditions of Contract Item 19 shall be deleted.

(h)   The application of Articles 1.6 1.8 1.9 and 1.10 of the Scottish Arbitration Code 1999 shall be subject to the provisions of Addendum Clause A.2 of the Contract unless the Arbitrator otherwise directs.

Application to Northern Ireland   **12.3**   If the Works are situated in Northern Ireland the Contract shall in all respects be construed and operate as a Northern Irish contract and shall be interpreted in accordance with the law of Northern Ireland.

13   **CONSTRUCTION (DESIGN AND MANAGEMENT) REGULATIONS 1994**

Definitions   **13.1**   In this Clause

(a)   'the Regulations' means the Construction (Design and Management) Regulations 1994 or any statutory re-enactment or amendment thereof for the time being in force

(b)   'Planning Supervisor' and 'Principal Contractor' mean the persons so described in regulation 2(1) of the Regulations

(c)   'Health and Safety Plan' means the plan prepared by virtue of regulation 15 of the Regulations

Action to be taken   **13.2**   Where and to the extent that the Regulations apply to the Works and

(a)   the Engineer is appointed Planning Supervisor

and/or

(b)   the Contractor is appointed Principal Contractor

then in taking any action as such they shall state in writing that the action is being taken under the Regulations.

13.3   (1)   Any action under the Regulations taken by either the Planning Supervisor the Principal Contractor and in particular any alteration or amendment to the Health and Safety Plan shall be deemed to be an Engineer's instruction pursuant to Clause 2.3. Provided that the Contractor shall in no event be entitled to any additional payment and/or extension of time in respect of any such action to the extent that it results from any action lack of action or default on the part of the Contractor.

(2)   If any such action of either the Planning Supervisor or the Principal Contractor could not in the Contractor's opinion reasonably have been foreseen by an experienced contractor the Contractor shall as early as practicable give written notice thereof to the Engineer.

ADDENDUM A

AVOIDANCE AND SETTLEMENT OF DISPUTES

Avoidance of disputes **A.1** In order to overcome where possible the causes of disputes and in those cases where disputes are likely still to arise to facilitate their clear definition and early resolution (whether by agreement or otherwise) the following procedure shall apply for the avoidance and settlement of disputes.

Matters of **A.2** If at any time
dissatisfaction

(a)   the Contractor is dissatisfied with any act or instruction of the Resident Engineer or any other person responsible to the Engineer or

(b)   the Employer or the Contractor is dissatisfied with any decision opinion instruction direction certificate or valuation of the Engineer or with any other matter arising under or in connection with the Contract or the carrying out of the Works

the matter of dissatisfaction shall be referred to the Engineer who shall notify his written decision to the Employer and the Contractor within 14 days of the reference to him.

Disputes **A.3** The Employer and the Contractor agree that no matter shall constitute nor be said to give rise to a dispute unless and until in respect of that matter

(a)   the time for the giving of a decision by the Engineer on a matter of dissatisfaction under Clause A2 has expired or the decision given is unacceptable or has not been implemented and in consequence the Employer or the Contractor has served on the other and on the Engineer a notice in writing (hereinafter called the Notice of Dispute) or

(b)   an adjudicator has given a decision on a dispute under Clause A6 and the Employer or the Contractor is not giving effect to the decision and in consequence the other has served on him and the Engineer a Notice of Dispute

and the dispute shall be that stated in the Notice of Dispute. For the purposes of all matters arising under or in connection with the Contract or the carrying out of the Works the word 'dispute' shall be construed accordingly and shall include any difference.

A.4 (a)   Notwithstanding the existence of a dispute following the service of a Notice under Clause A.3 and unless the Contract has already been determined or abandoned the Employer and the Contractor shall continue to perform their obligations.

(b)   The Employer and the Contractor shall give effect forthwith to every decision of

(i)   the Engineer on a matter of dissatisfaction given under Clause A.2 and

(ii)   the adjudicator on a dispute given under Clause A.6

unless and until that decision is revised by agreement of the Employer and Contractor or pursuant to Addendum A.

Conciliation A.5 (a) The Employer or the Contractor may at any time before service of a Notice to Refer to arbitration under Clause A.9 by notice in writing seek the agreement of the other for the dispute to be considered under "The Institution of Civil Engineers' Conciliation Procedure (1999)" or any amendment or modification thereof being in force at the date of such notice.

(b) If the other party agrees to this procedure any recommendation of the conciliator shall be deemed to have been accepted as finally determining the dispute by agreement so that the matter is no longer in dispute unless a Notice of Adjudication under Clause A.6 or a Notice to Refer to arbitration under Clause A.9 has been served in respect of that dispute not later than 1 month after receipt of the recommendation by the dissenting party.

Adjudication A.6 (a) The Employer and the Contractor each has the right to refer any dispute as to a matter under the Contract for adjudication and either party may give notice in writing (hereinafter called the Notice of Adjudication) to the other at any time of his intention so to do. The adjudication shall be conducted under "The Institution of Civil Engineers' Adjudication Procedure (1997)" or any amendment or modification thereof being in force at the time of the said Notice.

(b) Unless the adjudicator has already been appointed he is to be appointed by a timetable with the object of securing his appointment and referral of the dispute to him within 7 days of such notice.

(c) The adjudicator shall reach a decision within 28 days of referral or such longer period as is agreed by the parties after the dispute has been referred.

(d) The adjudicator may extend the period of 28 days by up to 14 days with the consent of the party by whom the dispute was referred.

(e) The adjudicator shall act impartially.

(f) The adjudicator may take the initiative in ascertaining the facts and the law.

A.7 The decision of the adjudicator shall be binding until the dispute is finally determined by legal proceedings or by arbitration (if the contract provides for arbitration or the parties otherwise agree to arbitration) or by agreement.

A.8 The adjudicator is not liable for anything done or omitted in the discharge or purported discharge of his functions as adjudicator unless the act or omission is in bad faith and any employee or agent of the adjudicator is similarly not liable.

Arbitration A.9 (a) All disputes arising under or in connection with the Contract or the carrying out of the Works other than failure to give effect to a decision of an adjudicator shall be finally determined by reference to arbitration. The party seeking arbitration shall serve on the other party a notice in writing (called the Notice to Refer) to refer the dispute to arbitration.

(b) Where an adjudicator has given a decision under Clause A6 in respect of the particular dispute the Notice to Refer must be served within three months of the giving of the decision otherwise it shall be final as well as binding.

Appointment of arbitrator A.10

(a) The arbitrator shall be a person appointed by agreement of the parties.

President or Vice-President to act

(b) If the parties fail to appoint an arbitrator within one month of either party serving on the other party a notice in writing (hereinafter called the Notice to Concur) to concur in the appointment of an arbitrator the dispute shall be referred to a person to be appointed on the application of either party by the President for the time being of The Institution of Civil Engineers.

(c) If an arbitrator declines the appointment or after appointment is removed by order of a competent court or is incapable of acting or dies and the parties do not within one month of the vacancy arising fill the vacancy then either party may apply to the President for the time being of The Institution of Civil Engineers to appoint another arbitrator to fill the vacancy.

(d) In any case where the President for the time being of The Institution of Civil Engineers is not able to exercise the functions conferred on him by this Clause the said functions shall be exercised on his behalf by a Vice-President for the time being of the said Institution.

Arbitration–procedure and powers A.11

(a) Any reference to arbitration under this Clause shall be deemed to be a submission to arbitration within the meaning of the Arbitration Act 1996 or any statutory re-enactment or amendment thereof for the time being in force. The reference shall be conducted in accordance with the procedure set out in the Appendix to the Conditions of Contract or any amendment or modification thereof being in force at the time of the appointment of the arbitrator. Such arbitrator shall have full power to open up review and revise any decision opinion instruction direction certificate or valuation of the Engineer or an adjudicator.

(b) Neither party shall be limited in the arbitration to the evidence or arguments put to the Engineer or to any adjudicator pursuant to Clause A.2 or A.6 respectively.

(c) The award of the arbitrator shall be binding on all parties.

(d) Unless the parties otherwise agree in writing any reference to arbitration may proceed notwithstanding that the Works are not then complete or alleged to be complete.

Witness A.12

(a) No decision opinion instruction direction certificate or valuation given by the Engineer shall disqualify him from being called as a witness and giving evidence before a conciliator adjudicator or arbitrator on any matter whatsoever relevant to the dispute.

(b) All matters and information placed before a conciliator pursuant to a reference under Clause A.5 shall be deemed to be submitted to him without prejudice and the conciliator shall not be called as witness by the parties or anyone claiming through them in connection with any adjudication arbitration or other legal proceedings arising out of or connected with any matter so referred to him.

ICE Conditions of Contract for Minor Works

APPENDIX TO THE CONDITIONS OF CONTRACT
(to be prepared before tenders are invited and to be included with the documents supplied to prospective tenderers)

1. Short description of the work to be carried out under the Contract

   ....

   ....

   ....

2. The payment to be made under Article 2 of the Agreement in accordance with Clause 7 will be ascertained on the following basis.

   (a) * Lump sum

   (b) * Measure and value using a priced Bill of Quantities

   (c) * Valuation based on a Schedule of Rates (with an indication in the Schedule of the approximate quantities of major items)

   (d) * Valuation based on a Daywork Schedule

   (e) * Cost plus (the cost is to be specifically defined in the Contract and will exclude off-site overheads and profit)

   * *The alternatives not being used are to be deleted. Two or more bases for payment may be used on one Contract.*

3. Where a Bill of Quantities or a Schedule of Rates is provided the method of measurement used is

   ....

4. Name of Engineer (Clause 2. 1)

   ....

5. Starting date (if known) (Clause 4. 1)

   ....

6. Period for completion (Clause 4.2)

   ....

7　　Period for completion of parts of the Works if applicable and details of the work to be carried out within each such part (Clause 4.2)

	Details of work	Period for completion
Part A	....	....
Part B	....	....
Part C	....	....

8　　Liquidated damages (Clause 4.6)

....

9　　Limit of liquidated damages (Clause 4.6)

....

10　　Defects Correction Period (Clause 5. 1)

....

11　　Rate of retention (Clause 7.3)

....

12　　Limit of retention (Clause 7.3)

....

13　　Minimum amount of interim certificate (Clause 7.3)

....

14　　Bank whose base lending rate is to be used (Clause 7.8)

....

15　　Insurance of the Works (Clause 10. 1)

Required/Not required [a]

16　　Minimum amount of third party insurance (persons and property) (Clause 10.6)

....

for each and every occurrence

17　　Name of the Planning Supervisor (Clause 13(1)(b))

....

Address ....

....

18　　Name of the Principal Contractor (Clause 13(1)(b))

....

Address ....

....

19   The Arbitration Procedure to be used is (Clause A.11(a))

(a) "The Institution of Civil Engineers' Arbitration Procedure (1997)"[a]

or

(b) "The Construction Industry Model Arbitration Rules "[a]

If no deletion is made "The Institution of Civil Engineers' Arbitration Procedure (1997)" shall be used.

[a]   *Delete as appropriate.*

ICE Conditions of Contract for Minor Works

AGREEMENT

THIS AGREEMENT is made the .... day of ....20 ......

between ....

of (or whose registered office is at)..

....

(called the 'Employer') of the one part

and...

of (or whose registered office is at)..

....

(called the 'Contractor') of the other part

WHEREAS the Employer wishes to have carried out the following ....

....

....

and has accepted a Tender by the Contractor for the same

NOW IT IS HEREBY AGREED AS FOLLOWS:

Article 1
The Contractor will subject to the Conditions of Contract perform and complete the Works.

Article 2
The Employer will pay the Contractor such sum or sums as shall become payable under the Contract and in accordance with the Conditions of Contract.

Article 3
The following documents shall be deemed to form and be read and construed as part of this agreement namely:-

The Contractor's Tender (excluding any general or printed terms contained or referred to therein unless expressly agreed in writing to be incorporated in the Contract)

The Conditions of Contract

The Appendix to the Conditions of Contract

The Drawings. Reference numbers ....

....

....

The Specification. Reference ....

The priced Bill of Quantities*

The Schedule of Rates*

The Daywork Schedules*

The following extra documents *

from ....to ....dated ....

from ....to ....dated ....

from ....to ....dated ....

from ....to ....dated.......................

SIGNED on behalf of the said ....Ltd/plc (the Employer)

Signature...

Position...

In the presence of..

SIGNED on behalf of the said .... Ltd/plc (the Contractor)

Signature…...

Position..

In the presence of..

* *Delete if not applicable*